CW00348650

falling in Love

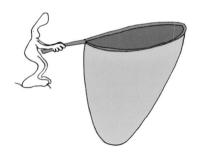

Published by MQ Publications Limited
12 The Ivories, 6–8 Northampton Street, London N1 2HY
Tel: 020 7359 2244 / Fax: 020 7359 1616
email: mail@mqpublications.com

ISBN: 1-84072-446-3

1 3 5 7 9 0 8 6 4 2

Printed and bound in China

falling in Love

BY LISA SWERLING & RALPH LAZAR

HAROLD'S PLANET MQP
MQ Publications Ltd

Alone at his desk,
late at night,
the writer
wonders...

How do people
fall in love

growing watermelon

GROWING watermelo...

Desperately he throws it from
the shady cliffs

And it shatter...
plain below,

and dancing to ...

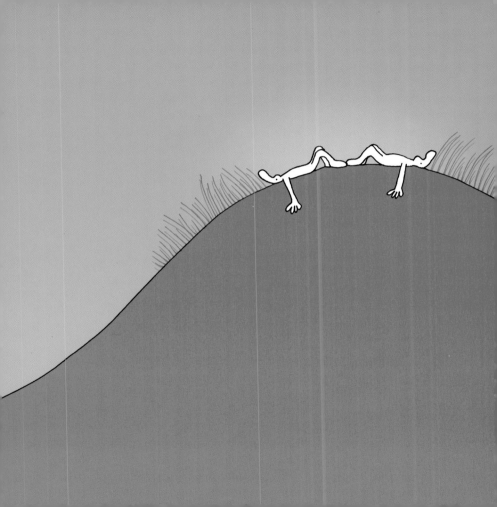

...and simultaneously sneezing in the spring of life.

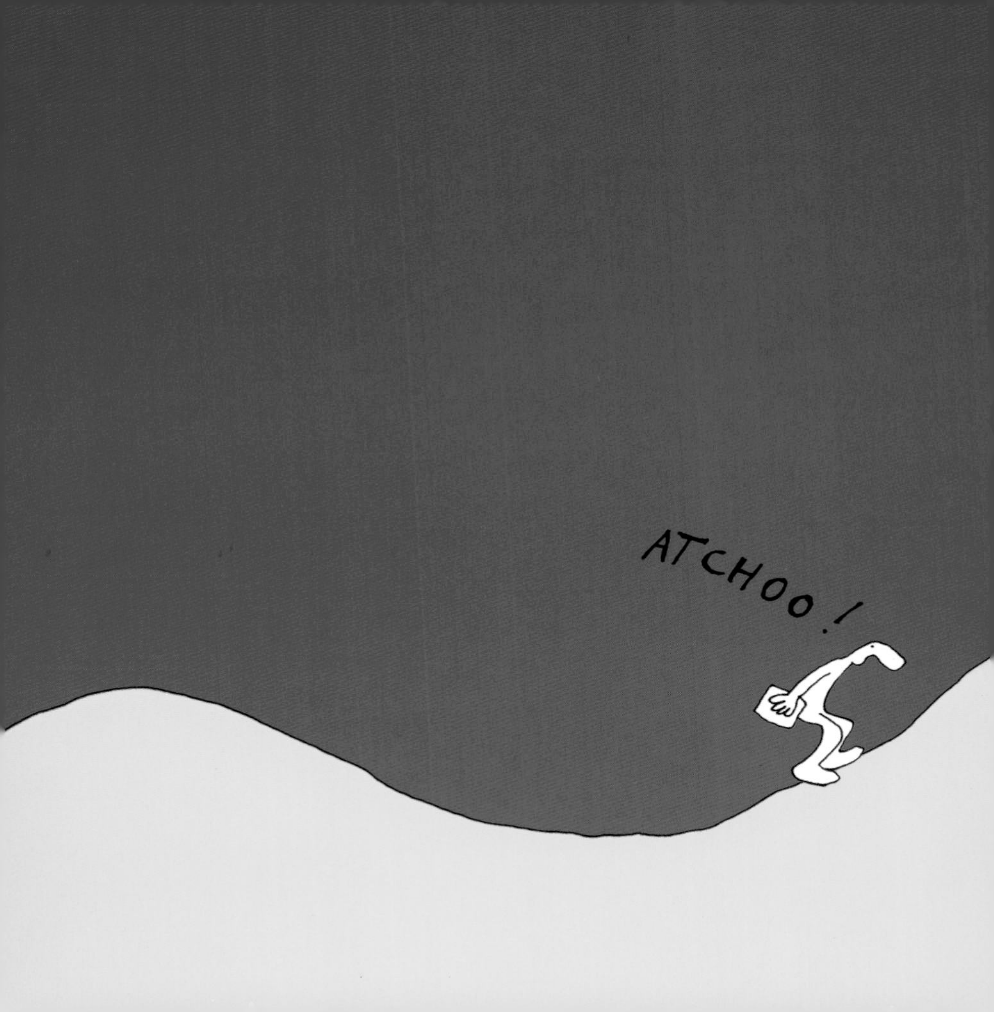
ATCHOO!

Some people
fall in love by
slipping on the
same banana
skin ...

... or growing watermelons.

One of the things still to

be considered is the

Gabes overall effect of

watermelons on

Super as a

whole?

SHE   Sh

Two   Isn't it

oralle

Hummagreeca

How people fall in love:

- ☑ grass
- ☑ sneeze
- ☑ bananas
- ☑ toast
- ☑ watermelons

I think I'm getting somewhere

Hula- hooping in time...

... Falling
head
over
heels ...

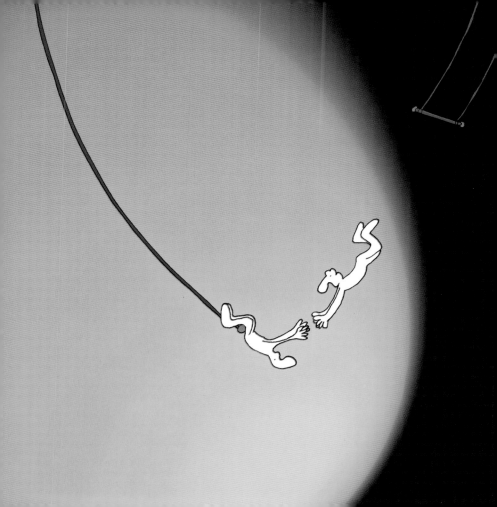

...and trusting in Fate.

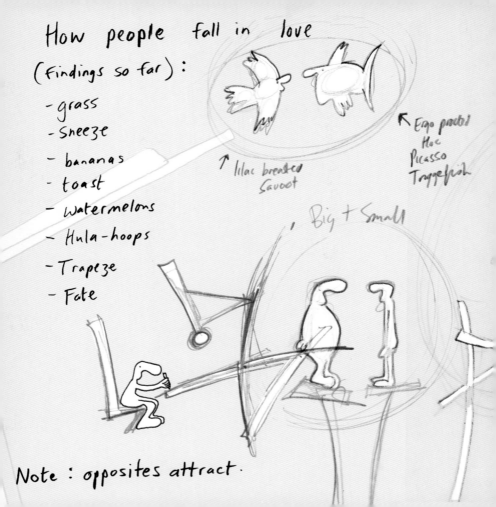

Some
just take
the
plunge ...

...ending up together
in a sea of possibilities...

... exploring the
unknown ...

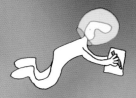

...sharing
an outlook...

... and dreaming
the same dream.

On rainbow watch...

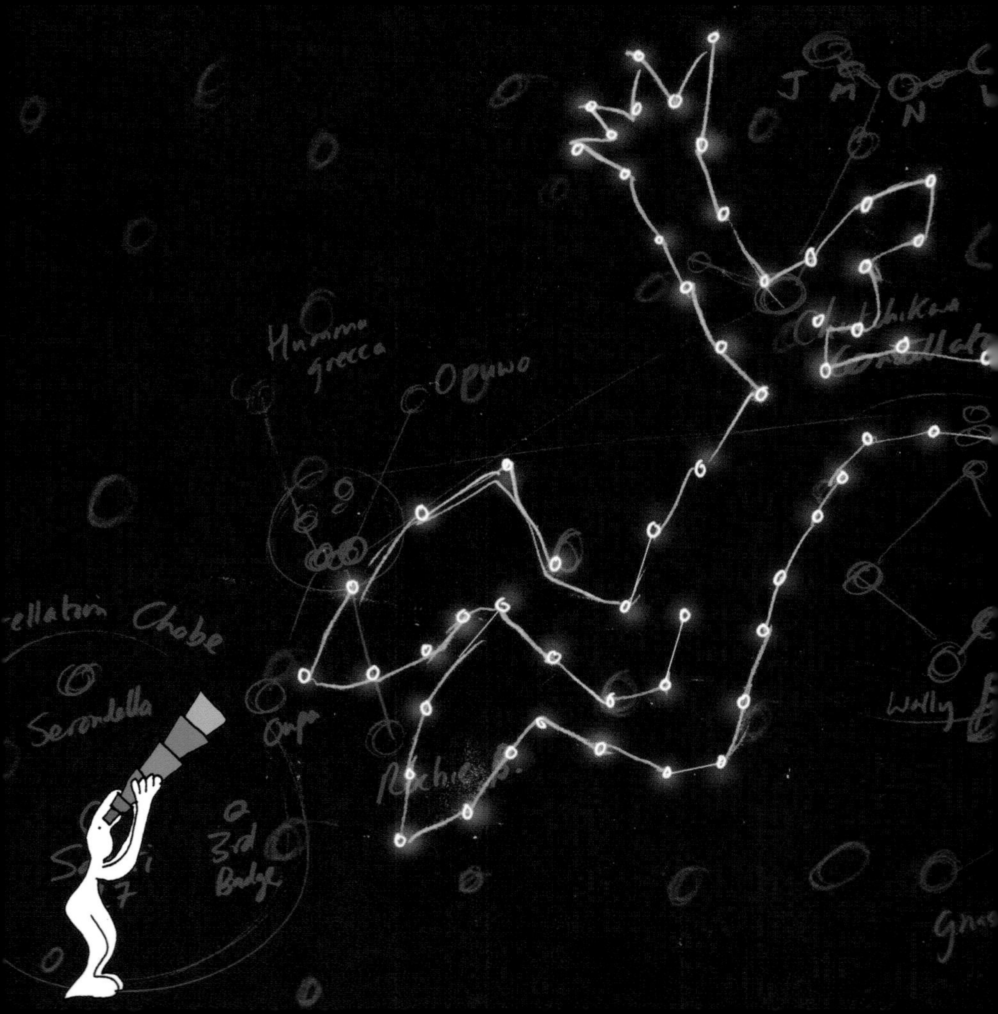

J
M
N
Opuwo
Chobe
Serondella
Richie B.
3rd Bridge
Wally

... and talking deep into the night.

Note for further research: The
excavation of long-forgotten
conversations

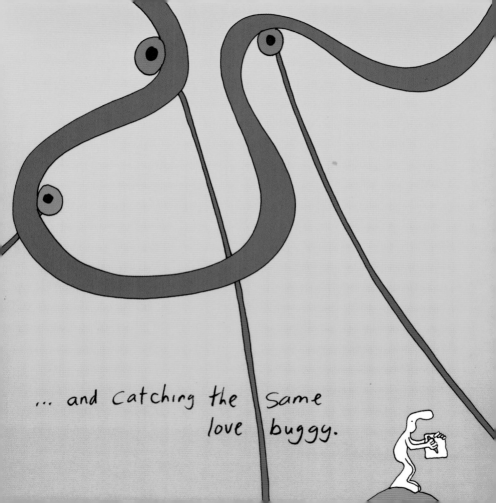

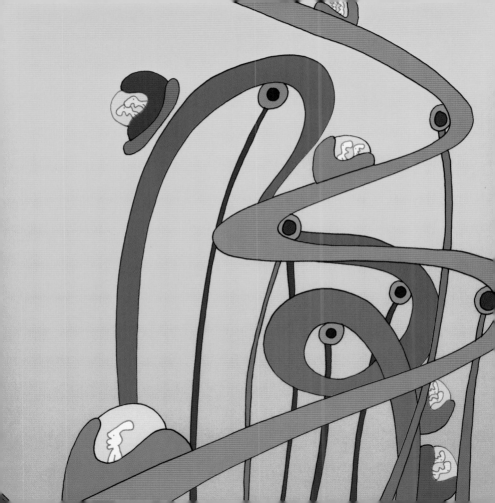

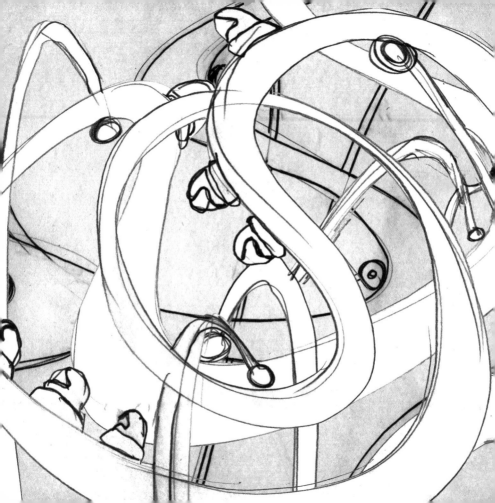

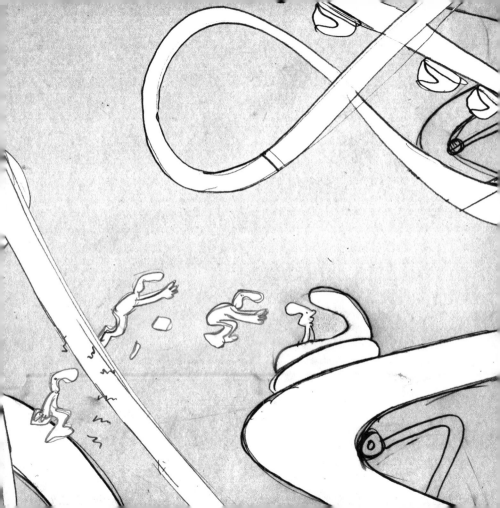

ABOUT THE AUTHORS

Ralph Lazar, Lisa Swerling and their daughter Bea are currently based in the UK. They have recently applied for visas to Harold's Planet, and are expected to move there as soon as the paperwork has been processed.

This book is for Ouma